Rampage in Prince's Garden

You can read more stories about
the gang from Buffin Street by
collecting the rest of the series.

For complete list, look at
the back of the book.

Rampage in Prince's Garden

Francesca Simon

Illustrated by Emily Bolam

Orion
Children's Books

Rampage in Prince's Garden
first appeared in *Miaow Miaow Bow Wow*
first published in Great Britain in 2000
by Orion Children's Books
This edition first published in Great Britain in 2011
by Orion Children's Books
a division of the Orion Publishing Group Ltd
Orion House
5 Upper St Martin's Lane
London WC2H 9EA
An Hachette UK Company

1 3 5 7 9 10 8 6 4 2

Printed in China

The Orion Publishing Group's policy is to use papers that are natural,
renewable and recyclable products made from wood grown in sustainable forests.
The logging and manufacturing processes are expected to conform
to the environmental regulations of the country of origin.

www.orionbooks.co.uk

For Emily Lethbridge

BUFFIN STREET

Hello from everyone

Prince

Flick

Millie

Lola

Woof

Honey

Snuffle snuffle

Lily

Caw Caw

Do-Re-Mi

Rustle rustle

Jogger

Growl

Sour Puss

Miaow

Joey

Bow wow

Dizzy

Miaow

Kit

Squeak

Squeak

Doris

Boris

Fang

Woof

Welcome to Buffin Street!

Come and join all the Buffin Street
dogs, cats, rabbits, puppies and parrots,
and find out what *really* goes on when
their people are out of sight...

"Prince has gone!" said Fang.
"I saw him drive away!"

"Where's he gone?"
asked Honey.
"He was bathed and
clipped yesterday."

"He's gone to his other house," said Millie. "He has two, remember?"

Prince lived in Buffin Street for
half the week, then somewhere
else for the rest. His people
shared him between them.

Prince quite liked having two houses.
"Twice the food, twice the presents,"
he always said, preening at his rows
of bows, his two sparkling diamond
collars and sacks full of toys.

Lola stretched and peered
over her balcony.

"They've left the gate open!"

Everyone stood still as
this amazing news sank in.

"Is anyone home?"
asked Millie finally.

"Don't think so," said Lola.

"Are you sure?"
said Sour Puss.

The one time she'd tried
to sneak into Prince's garden
she'd been sprayed by a hose.

"Sure I'm sure,"
said Lola, yawning.

"I've always wanted to see Prince's secret garden," said Fang.

"Me too," said Honey.

The animals looked at each other.

"Do you think we should?"
said Millie.

"Sure!" said Fang.
He ran to the gate and pushed it.

Cr-eeeeak!

went the old gate as
it swung open.

"Come on!" said Fang.

The animals looked
at one another.

"We'll just take a quick peep,
and then leave," said Lola.

"No harm in that," said Dizzy,
his tail thumping wildly.

"Yeah," said Honey.

"No one will even know we've
been there," said Millie.
In they sneaked.

"Wow!"

said Fang.

32

"Wow!"

said Lola, Dizzy,
Honey, Millie
and Lily.

There was a perfect, newly
mown circle of lawn, with
stepping stones, and little hills,
and a bridge.

And there was a goldfish
pond, statues, piles of
raked autumn leaves,
and best of all, lots of
freshly-dug flower beds.

Millie explored the flower beds.

Fang found the perfect
spot to hide a bone.

Lily and her bunnies
started a new tunnel.

Dizzy frolicked in the leaves,
chasing his tail.

"It!" shouted Honey,
tapping Dizzy.

Dizzy chased after her.

Then Fang joined in.

And then Millie.

They bounced and scampered,
they zoomed and charged, racing and
chasing through the leaves and flowers.

Finally, they all collapsed out of
breath on the little bridge.

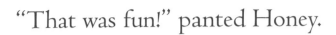

"That was fun!" panted Honey.

"Yeah," said Dizzy.

"Uh oh,"
said Millie.

"What?" said Honey.

"Look," said Millie.

"Uh oh,"
said Honey

"Uh oh,"

said Dizzy.

Somehow the garden
was wrecked.

"How did that happen?"
said Millie.

"We were so careful,"
said Honey.

"What'll we do?"
wailed Lily.

Fang took charge.
"Let's tidy up quick, before
Prince gets back," he ordered.
"Many paws make short work."

The animals smoothed and
shaped, tidied and trimmed,
as fast as they could.

"There!" said Dizzy.
"Perfect!" said Fang.
A car door slammed.
"Let's get outta here!" barked Fang.

Zip!

"No one will ever know!"
said Honey.

But I am not sure that
she was right.

Bow wow
follow me

Did you enjoy exploring Prince's garden? Can you remember all the things that happened in the story?

Where do the animals think Prince has gone?

Why does Prince like having
two houses?

Who notices that the garden gate
has been left open?

What happened once when Sour Puss
tried to sneak into Prince's garden?

What do the animals say when they
get inside the garden?

Who finds the perfect spot
to hide a bone?

Who starts a new tunnel?

What happens when the animals
hear Prince coming back?

For more adventures with the
Buffin Street Gang, look out for
the other books in the series.

Meet
the Gang

Yum Yum

Jogger's Big Adventure

Miaow Miaow Bow Wow

The Haunted House of Buffin Street

Look at Me